The Flute Playlist

50 Popular Classics
in Easy Arrangements

Arranged by
Barrie Carson Turner

ED 13870
ISMN 979-0-2201-3703-7
ISBN 978-1-84761-409-4

www.schott-music.com

Mainz · London · Madrid · Paris · New York · Tokyo · Beijing
© 2016 Schott Music Ltd, London · Printed in Germany

PDF piano parts are available to download from www.schott-music.com (ED 13870).

Des parties d'accompagnent être téléchargés gratuitement à l'adresse
www.schott-music.com (ED 13870).

PDF-Dateien mit den Klavierstimmen sind als kostenloser Download unter
www.schott-music.com (ED 13870) erhältlich.

Please visit **www.schott-music.com/online-material** to download all audio files
for free using the following voucher code: **playlistfl**

Sur le site **www.schott-music.com/online-material** vous pouvez accéder et télécharger
gratuitement toutes les pistes audio en utilisant le code suivant : **playlistfl**

Auf der Website **www.schott-music.com/online-material** können alle Audio-Dateien
mit dem folgenden Gutscheincode kostenlos heruntergeladen werden: **playlistfl**

ED 13870
British Library Cataloguing-in-Publication Data.
A catalogue record for this book is available from the British Library
ISMN 979-0-2201-3703-7
ISBN 978-1-84761-409-4

Cover design by www.josellopis.com
Prelim design and typesetting by www.adamhaystudio.com
Music setting and page layout by Scott Barnard (www.musicpreparation.co.uk)
Printed in the UK S&Co. 9312

Contents

1. Adagietto
from Symphony No. 5

Gustav Mahler (1860-1911)
Arr. Barrie Carson Turner

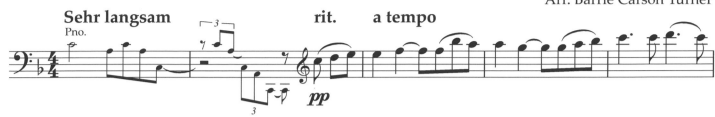

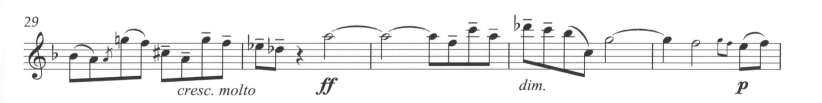

© 2016 Schott Music Ltd, London

2. Air
from Suite No. 3, BWV 1068

Johann Sebastian Bach (1685-1750)
Arr. Barrie Carson Turner

Andante

3. Andante
from Piano Concerto No. 23, K488

Wolfgang Amadeus Mozart (1756-1791)
Arr. Barrie Carson Turner

4. The Blue Danube

Johann Strauss II (1825-1899)
Arr. Barrie Carson Turner

5. Clair de Lune
from *Suite Bergamasque*

Claude Debussy (1862-1918)
Arr. Barrie Carson Turner

6. Canon

Johann Pachelbel (1653-1706)
Arr. Barrie Carson Turner

7. Chanson de Matin

Edward Elgar (1857-1934)
Arr. Barrie Carson Turner

8. Chorus of the Hebrew Slaves
from *Nabucco*

Giuseppe Verdi (1813-1901)
Arr. Barrie Carson Turner

9. The Dance of the Little Swans
from *Swan Lake*

Pyotr Ilyich Tchaikovsky (1840-1893)
Arr. Barrie Carson Turner

Allegro moderato
Pno.

To Coda

D.S. al Coda　　*Coda*

10. Dance of the Blessed Spirits
from *Orpheus and Eurydice*

Christoph Willibald Gluck (1714-1787)
Arr. Barrie Carson Turner

11. Danse Macabre

Camille Saint-Saëns (1835-1921)
Arr. Barrie Carson Turner

Mouvement modere de valse

12. The Pearl Fishers' Duet

from *Les pêcheurs de perles*

Georges Bizet (1838-1875)
Arr. Barrie Carson Turner

13. Emperor Concerto
2nd Movement

Ludwig van Beethoven (1770-1827)
Arr. Barrie Carson Turner

Adagio un poco mosso

14. Flower Duet

from *Lakmé*

Léo Delibes (1836-1891)
Arr. Barrie Carson Turner

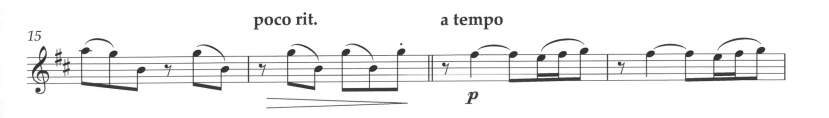

15. Gavotte
from *Holberg Suite*

Edvard Grieg (1843-1907)
Arr. Barrie Carson Turner

16. Gymnopédie No. 1

Erik Satie (1866-1925)
Arr. Barrie Carson Turner

Lent et douloureux

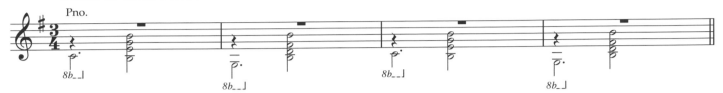

17. Habanera
from *Carmen*

Georges Bizet (1838-1875)
Arr. Barrie Carson Turner

18. Hallelujah Chorus
from *Messiah*

George Frideric Handel (1685-1759)
Arr. Barrie Carson Turner

19. Hornpipe
from *Water Music*

George Frideric Handel (1685-1759)
Arr. Barrie Carson Turner

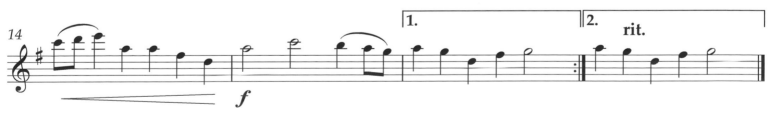

20. Impromptu
Op. 90, No. 3

Franz Schubert (1797-1828)
Arr. Barrie Carson Turner

21. Intermezzo
from *Cavalleria rusticana*

Pietro Mascagni (1863-1945)
Arr. Barrie Carson Turner

22. Jerusalem

Hubert Parry (1848-1918)
Arr. Barrie Carson Turner

23. Jupiter
from *The Planets*

Gustav Holst (1874-1934)
Arr. Barrie Carson Turner

24. Intermezzo
from *Karelia Suite*

Jean Sibelius (1865-1957)
Arr. Barrie Carson Turner

25. Liebesträume No. 3

Franz Liszt (1811-1886)
Arr. Barrie Carson Turner

26. Menuet
from *Sonatine*

Maurice Ravel (1875-1937)
Arr. Barrie Carson Turner

27. Menuetto
from Symphony No. 104 (London)

Joseph Haydn (1732-1809)
Arr. Barrie Carson Turner

28. Méditation
from *Thaïs*

Jules Massenet (1842-1912)
Arr. Barrie Carson Turner

29. Morning
from *Peer Gynt*

Edvard Grieg (1843-1907)
Arr. Barrie Carson Turner

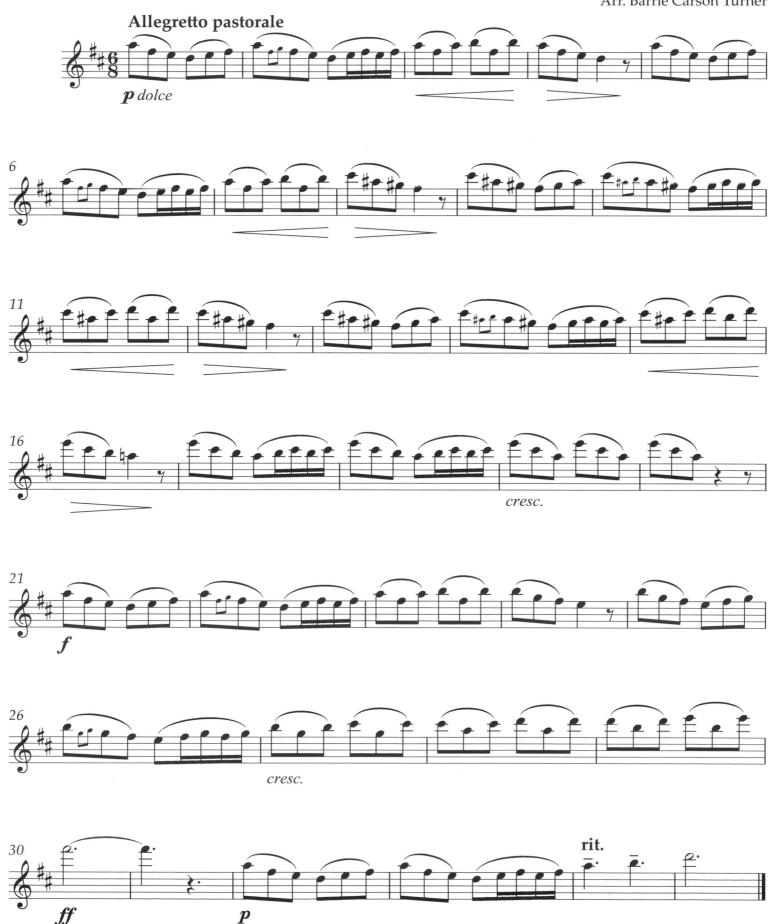

30. Ode to Joy
from Symphony No. 9

Ludwig van Beethoven (1770-1827)
Arr. Barrie Carson Turner

Allegro assai

31. Nessun Dorma
from *Turandot*

Giacomo Puccini (1858-1924)
Arr. Barrie Carson Turner

32. Nimrod
from *Enigma* Variations

Edward Elgar (1857-1934)
Arr. Barrie Carson Turner

33. Nocturne
Op. 9, No. 2

Frédéric Chopin (1810-1849)
Arr. Barrie Carson Turner

34. Non più andrai
from *The Marriage of Figaro*

Wolfgang Amadeus Mozart (1756-1791)
Arr. Barrie Carson Turner

35. O Mio Babbino Caro
from *Gianni Schicchi*

Giacomo Puccini (1858-1924)
Arr. Barrie Carson Turner

36. Dance of the Sugar Plum Fairy
from *The Nutcracker*

Pyotr Ilyich Tchaikovsky (1840-1893)
Arr. Barrie Carson Turner

37. Prélude à l'après-midi d'un faune

Claude Debussy (1862-1918)
Arr. Barrie Carson Turner

Très modéré

38. Ride of the Valkyries
from *Die Walküre*

Richard Wagner (1813-1883)
Arr. Barrie Carson Turner

39. Spring
from *The Four Seasons*

Antonio Vivaldi (1678-1741)
Arr. Barrie Carson Turner

40. Symphony No. 1
4th movement

Johannes Brahms (1833-1897)
Arr. Barrie Carson Turner

41. The Old Castle
from *Pictures at an Exhibition*

Modest Mussorgsky (1839-1881)
Arr. Barrie Carson Turner

42. The Swan
from *The Carnival of the Animals*

Camille Saint-Saëns (1835-1921)
Arr. Barrie Carson Turner

Andantino grazioso

43. The Trout

Franz Schubert (1797-1828)
Arr. Barrie Carson Turner

44. Träumerei
from *Scenes from Childhood*, Op. 15

Robert Schumann (1810-1856)
Arr. Barrie Carson Turner

45. Toreador Song
from *Carmen*

Georges Bizet (1838-1875)
Arr. Barrie Carson Turner

46. Violin Concerto
2nd Movement

Felix Mendelssohn Bartholdy (1809-1847)
Arr. Barrie Carson Turner

47. Vltava
from *Má Vlast*

Bedřich Smetana (1824-1884)
Arr. Barrie Carson Turner

Allegro commodo non agitato

48. Waltz
from *Coppélia*

Léo Delibes (1836-1891)
Arr. Barrie Carson Turner

49. When I Am Laid in Earth

from *Dido and Aeneas*

Henry Purcell (1659-1695)
Arr. Barrie Carson Turner

50. Waltz
Op. 39, No. 15

Johannes Brahms (1833-1897)
Arr. Barrie Carson Turner

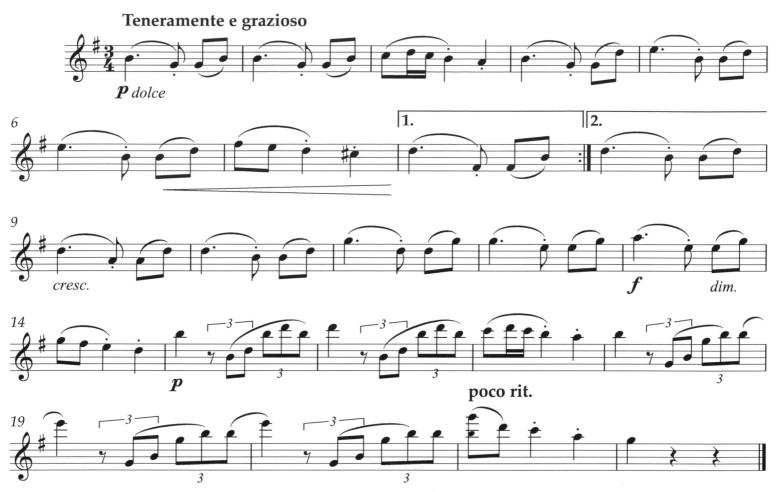